I EAT SQUIRRELS

A COLLECTION OF POETRY
FOR STRANGE CHILDREN

WRITTEN AND DRAWN BY

A. F. HARROLD

For Jack,

buy this book, please.

— sgnt.

2·2

D1642676

Books for grown ups by the same author

Poetry
Logic And The Heart (Love Poems 1999-2003)
Of Birds & Bees (*limited edition*)
Flood

Entertainments
Postcards From The Hedgehog
The Man Who Spent Years In The Bath
The Education of Epitome Quirkstandard

First published in the UK in 2009 by

Quirkstandard's Alternative
1 Cranbourne Gardens
Reading
Berkshire
RG30 6TS

www.afharrold.co.uk
www.quirkstandardsalternative.co.uk

Cover design and layout by Richard Ponsford

ISBN-13: 978-0-9557081-3-8

Printed and bound by CPI Group (UK) Ltd, Croydon, CR0 ¥Y

For Rob and Emma Sowden

To Leela.

Enjoy those poems!

May 2019.

Acknowledgements

Some of these poems first appeared, sometimes in slightly different forms, in the following places: **Postcards From The Hedgehog** (*Two Rivers Press*, 2007) – Fairy Tale Poem; Centipede; Autumn; Nursery Rhyme Poem; Jim & The Lion; Parrots Are Not To Be Confused With Dogs; The Mouse's Mistake; Giraffes Sitting Down; Polar Bears & Penguins; William's Song – **The Man Who Spent Years In The Bath** (*Quirkstandard's Alternative*, 2008) – Jam; Shark Poem; Bath Poem – **Revels Without Applause** (*Strange & Saturday*, 2003) – Mealtimes.

Contents

Fairy Tale Poem

When I was just an Ugly Duckling
I asked my mother
'What will I be?
Will I be handsome?
Will I be a swan?'
Here's what she said to me.

'No, you'll be a duck.
Just a particularly ugly one.'

very ugly baby →

QUACK!

A Poem About Some Food

I eat pizza,
I eat bread,
I eat toast
when I'm in bed,

I eat soup
with a ladle,
I eat meat
at the table,

I eat apples,
I eat pears,
I eat fruit
in many chairs,

I eat beans,
I eat rice,
I eat any–
thing that's nice.

I eat cows,
I eat sheep.
I eat chickens
going cheep.

I eat pasta,
I eat peas,
I eat things
that live in trees.

I eat squirrels,
I eat birds,
I have seconds,
I have thirds.

I eat lettuce,
I eat carrots,
I eat multi–
coloured parrots.

I eat anything
that moves –
I eat trotters,
I eat hooves,

I eat legs,
and I eat thighs,
I eat brains,
and I eat eyes.

I eat hearts
and I eat lungs.
Given gravy
I'd eat tongues.

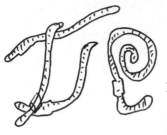

I eat spiders,
I eat flies,
I eat worms,
when baked in pies.

I eat crisps
and I eat biscuits.
Eat a hedgehog?
Of course I'd risk it.

I eat things
that I can't name –
when I get sick
I don't know what to blame.
So I eat it all again.

I eat hot things.
I eat cold.
But I won't do
as I am told –

'Eat your sprouts,'
my mother said.
Brussels sprouts?
I'd rather be dead.

Very Bad Dream Poem

I dreamt I woke up and I dreamt that I rose
and I dreamt I got dressed in my ordinary clothes
and I dreamt I had breakfast, went out to the hall
and I dreamt of my shoes and the walk into school.

And I dreamt of my teacher and I dreamt of my class
and I dreamt of some tests that were hard ones to pass
and I dreamt of school dinners and I dreamt I was sick
and I dreamt I forgot my PE kit.

I dreamt of the cold as I ran in my vest
and then I went home with a chill on my chest
and I dreamt that I sneezed while eating my dinner –
with snot on my plate the dream wasn't a winner.

I dreamt of my bath and I dreamt of my bed
and I dreamt I lay down my sleepy old head
and I dreamt that I dreamt that I dreamt and then...

well then I woke up... and it started again.

Jam

What are jammy dodgers dodging?
Presumably things that would otherwise lodge in
the jam in the middle or the biscuity bit.
I guess that's it.

Glasses

I went for a free eye test
at the optimist's the other day.

He said things were looking up.

Girls and Boys

Sugar and spice
and all things nice
that's not what girls
are made of...

it's brains and shins
and other things,
like guts and heart
and other parts,
like liver and spleen
and the bits in-between,
and hands and eyes
and brains and thighs
and blood and hair
and bones within
all wrapped up in skin
that's what girls are made of,

and boys too,
the recipe's pretty much the same
for both genders.

Miss V. V. Higginsworth-Smythe
A Cautionary Tale

Veronica Verulam Higginsworth-Smythe
stole sweets from shops and told fat lies.
She tripped up grannies and ran away
and swore at a Vicar trying to pray.

Veronica Verulam Higginsworth-Smythe
stuck chewing gum onto her school desk's side.
She pushed her sister into a puddle
and got her maths teacher into a muddle.

Veronica Verulam Higginsworth-Smythe
was willing to hire herself as a spy,
learn all the secrets from anyone's gang
and swap them for cash without a pang.

Veronica Verulam Higginsworth-Smythe
had a habit for making her small brother cry.
She poisoned a pelican, drew on the cat,
and was once very sick in her grandfather's hat.

Veronica Verulam Higginsworth-Smythe
consistently felt good inside
'cause she only did things she felt were fun
like teaching the meaning of slang to her mum.

You've heard enough now to understand why
Miss Veronica V. Higginsworth-Smythe
was sent by her parents to work in a mine
for tuppence a day for a very long time.

*

Veronica Verulam Higginsworth-Smythe
will work in the dark until she dies.
Veronica Verulam Higginsworth-Smythe.
Veronica Verulam Higginsworth-Smythe.

9

Playing With Pets

Some children play fetch with their dogs
and they spoil them with all their love;
some kids play catch with hedgehogs
but they only spoil their gloves.

Shark Poem

If you believe the fact that in the shark
his bite being really much worse than his bark
doesn't stop him from being a very good pet,
tell that, I suggest, to the one-armed vet.

I Know I Should Be
At School

I know I should be at school
but I was followed by the cat
and I wouldn't be allowed
into class with that.

So I paused at the gate
and determined to come home
and once I got back here
I couldn't leave him on his own.

When I looked into his eyes
I could tell that he's just lonely
and I can't be cruel to animals
so it seems to me the only
  way I'll be able to go back
  to school is if we
  get another cat and then they'll
  keep each other
  company.

Don't you agree, mum?

The Mysterious Menagerie, Part One

i.

Great grey belly porker,
toothy yawning slug,
cow-nosed submarine,
giant in the mud,
unlikely ballerina
tip-toes underwater,
sleepy swampland-island,
river's favourite daughter.

ii.

Stripy-armoured tiny tiger,
pollen-pouched and humble,
a fairy-small furry flyer,
content to simply bumble.

iii.

Fish-chasing waiters,
waddling torpedoes,
ice-footed flipper-flappers,
swimmers with no speedos.

A Nice Tune

When Sidney the snake
decided to take
piano lessons
they lasted seconds.

Headbutting the keys
didn't please
Mrs Hosannah
who owned the piano.

She slammed the lid
which did for Sid.

Centipede

You can't impede the scent of a centipede
any more than a centipede can.

He's tried to wash more often,
in fact it's a personal goal,
but every time he turns on the tap
he's swept straight down the hole.

(I would draw a very small flannel
in the centipede's front hands,
but it would be so small you'd never
tell what it was, so I won't)

If I Woke Up As A Beetle

If I woke up as a beetle
my bed would be too big.
My breakfast wouldn't interest me,
I wouldn't give a fig –

A cornflake half the size of me?
I'd be scared that I'd drop it
and if mum saw a beetle on the table, well –
she'd attempt to swat it.

I wouldn't have to go to school though
'cause when I raised my hand
my teacher wouldn't notice me
and she wouldn't understand

because beetles can't speak English
and teachers can't speak Beetle.
So I'll stay at home instead
and if the weather's nice my feet'll

walk me round the garden
where I'll chat with other bugs
and with worms and centipedes
and with snails and flies and slugs.

Evolution In Action

I had two pets, once.
I had a rat and a cat,
but the cat used to look at the rat
in a certain way
that seemed to say
'I'm going to eat you up, one day'.

The rat grew understandably nervous
and took to hoarding bits of string,
scraps of cardboard, all sorts of things
and out of these he made two wings.

And so as to avoid the cat,
the clever and inventive rat learnt to fly,
though not too high,
since heights are scary
when you're small and brown and hairy
and not naturally given to flight
at any height.

But let us just say that
he flew higher than the cat could reach
at a stretch.

And so when I took my pets for a walk
by my side the cat would stalk
and up above us in the sky
my rat would fly,
attached to us by a very long bit of string
so he wouldn't get lost.

The cat was not too happy about all this
because he still longed to eat the rat
and was unimpressed (in that typically cattish way)
  that evolution
had driven the rat,
to avoid the teeth and claws of the cat,
to evolve and adapt
and become a bit of a bat.

Mealtimes

I'd sing for my supper
and I'd dance for my dinner,
I'd triumph over tragedy for tea,
I'd eloquently launch into lyrics for lunch
but I'll never break a date for brie.

Autumn

In the autumn of the year
only two things are clear,
the facts are these:
the leaves leave the trees
except for the evergreens
who leave their leaves in their eaves.

Mountain Poem

Give me a mountain
and I'll show you
a dangerous place to build a billiard ball factory.

Mountains. No good for round things — it's all downhill from here.

Not The Best Poem
In The World

If my imaginative powers were stronger
this poem would probably be longer.

Jennifer Jones

Jennifer Jones was a wonderful girl,
her cheeks were rosy, her hair could curl,
she'd skip about and sing and laugh
but on Friday nights she had her bath.

When her mother said 'Jenny, I'm running the water,'
a change came over her beautiful daughter.
She'd throw back her head and let out a shout
that would aggravate her granddad's gout.

Her hair would spike, she'd go red in the face,
she'd jump and she'd jump all over the place,
knocking down vases and scaring the cat,
the goldfish, the duck and her brother's pet rat.

Eventually
her mother gave up and got in herself
and had a long soak, which was good for her health.

Jennifer Jones is now nearly thirty
and has no friends at all because she's so dirty.

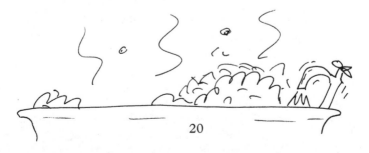

20

The Iced-Bun Song

Five iced-buns in the baker's shop.
One of them is sold to feed a hungry cop.

Four iced-buns on the baker's shelf.
One of them goes to a party with an elf.

Three iced-buns getting lonelier each day.
One gets a part in a Shakespeare play.

Two iced-buns in the baker's window.
One gets promoted and becomes a flamingo.

One iced-bun left all on its own –
talks to the other iced-buns on the phone.

(old-fashioned telephone)

Hello?

(Iced bun on a plate)

The Garden Party

I was looking out the window, what did I see?
  One wild wallaby sitting in the tree.

I was looking out the window, what do you think I saw?
  Two terrible tarantulas waiting at the door,
  and one wild wallaby sitting in the tree.

I was looking out the window, what do you think was there?
  Three thunderous thrushes flapping in the air,
  two terrible tarantulas waiting by the door
  and one wild wallaby sitting in the tree.

I looked out the window, what was it made me blink?
  Four furious flamingos turning ever so pink,
  three thunderous thrushes flapping in the air,
  two terrible tarantulas waiting by the door,
  and one wild wallaby sitting in the tree.

I looked out the window, what on earth was that?
  Five flaming ferrets talking to the cat,
  four furious flamingos turning ever so pink,
  three thunderous thrushes flapping in the air,
  two terrible tarantulas waiting by the door
  and one wild wallaby sitting in the tree.

I was looking out the window, what did I see?
  Six sneaky sea-lions staring back at me,
  five flaming ferrets talking to the cat,
  four furious flamingos turning ever so pink,
  three thunderous thrushes flapping in the air,
  two terrible tarantulas waiting by the door
  and one wild wallaby sitting in the tree.

I was looking out the window, what do you think I saw?
  Seven squeaking squids carried by a minotaur,
  six sneaky sea-lions staring back at me,
  five flaming ferrets talking to the cat,
  four furious flamingos turning ever so pink,
  three thunderous thrushes flapping in the air,
  two terrible tarantulas waiting by the door,
  and one wild wallaby sitting in the tree.

I looked out my window, what gave me a fright?
  Eight enormous elephants blocking out the light,
  seven squeaking squids carried by a minotaur,
  six sneaky sea-lions staring back at me,
  five flaming ferrets talking to the cat,
  four furious flamingos turning ever so pink,
  three thunderous thrushes flapping in the air,
  two terrible tarantulas waiting by the door,
  and one wild wallaby sitting in the tree.

I went out the back door and quickly ran away,
I went to my gran's and she said that I could stay.

I don't know what they want, they never seem to say,
but my gran drives past the house almost every single day –
she says they're all still there, though it doesn't seem right –
  eight enormous elephants blocking out the light,
  seven squeaking squids carried by a minotaur,
  six sneaky sea-lions staring back at me,
  five flaming ferrets talking to the cat,
  four furious flamingos turning ever so pink,
  three thunderous thrushes flapping in the air,
  two terrible tarantulas waiting by the door,
  and one wild wallaby sitting in the tree.

One day I'll go and ask what they all want with me.

Pancake

Pancakes are good.
Pancakes are great.
Pancake's a food
that I really rate.

Although it's not really much of a cake,
when you think about it,
more just a sort of floppy plate.

Fish

Why are fish so happy?
All they do is swim and feed.

But they never wear a nappy
so they swim in what they've peed.

A fish - happy
but disgusting

The Kids Of Class 4B
A Teacher's Lament

Class 4B is filled with freaks,
every kid is weird,
take Suzy, say, she looks okay,
but hides things in her beard.

Billy Jones is skin and bones
his elbows poke at angles,
next to him sits clanking Jim
who wears his mother's bangles.

Little Mary's strangely scary
toothy, tall and oddly hairy.
There's Elaine who comes from Spain
and leaves her homework on the plane.

Isadora is a snorer
if lessons are too dull,
and next to her is Jennifer
who has cobwebs in her skull.

Snore!

No one's finer than Jemima
she's practicing to be a miner –
swings her pick at little Rick
and when she hits he coughs up sick.

Little Francis always dances
adding up his sums,
then there's this pair Yvette and Cher
who whistle through their bums.

That there's Trevor, who's quite clever –
he chews his gum and wears his leather –
he sits with Sonny who gives him money
(saying 'No' to Trevor just isn't funny).

Graham Liszt is hardly missed –
he's not been to class for years.
Algernon Smith is sensitive
and spends all day in tears.

Juliet was sold a pet
cabbage – no one's told her yet.
Shy-boy Sid almost did
but he turned silent, ran and hid.

Lovely Jane is quite a pain –
she answers every question.
She lifts her hand like she understands
then makes a rubbish suggestion.

Isabelle is quite a girl,
six foot tall and broad as well.
Bob and Brian are always lying –
no one listens, but at least they're trying.

Jessica Wright stays up all night
and hides in shadows from sunlight.
Boris Stoker's quite a joker –
he got a stake and tried to poke her.

Big fat Cyril brings a squirrel
into class each day –
in his lunch-box he brings a fox
and at break time lets them play.

Oh! Class 4B, oh! Class 4B –
they're so much worse than I can say,
Oh! Class 4B, oh! Class 4B –
thank God I teach 4A.

What's Wrong With
Dinosaurs?

I was always disappointed to read about the dinosaurs
because everything I read said they were extinct
that struck me as a shame since some of them were herbivores
who wouldn't have caused harm to the smallest little mink –
so why are they extinct?

I mean,
I understand these days why we wouldn't want a Tyrannosaur
wandering about through the streets of London town
because everyone in the wqy would quickly become a snack
   or more
and a policeman would tut tut tut with his Special Service
   frown –

'Dinosaurs are a hazard,' he'd say, 'And I wouldn't recommend
anyone to attempt to have a dinosaur for a friend
or a pet or an acquaintance, they'd eat you as soon as that,'
and the T. Rex would then munch him from his boots up to
   his hat.

So I understand entirely why meat-eaters were removed
but I still ponder why on earth the herbivores are extinct,
why the brontosaurs and tricerotops and stegasaurs weren't
   approved
unless eating all that grass gave them breath that really stinks
(or maybe some other gas that really stinks).
So, maybe after all *that's* why they're extinct?

Stickboy

You've all heard of Stickboy,
the son of Stickman and Stickwoman,
that family of people who have sticks for bodies,
a ball for a head,
and more sticks for arms and legs.

People who can't draw very well
keep doing pictures of them.
They've grown rich on the royalties.
They live in a very nice house.
A very narrow house,
since they don't need much space,
but a very nice house all the same.

Stickboy has a pet dog, Rover.
Stickwoman, his mother,
lets them go and play in the park by themselves,
even though Stickboy is only seven.

'Aren't you worried,' everybody asks her,
'That he might get lost, or meet a stranger,
or have an accident?'

'Oh no,' explains his mother,
'He's a very good boy who knows the way,
and knows not to talk to strangers,
and besides he's with Rover, the dog.
All I have to do is shout 'Fetch'
at the edge of the park
and Rover will come running,
Stickboy clutched in his mouth.'

'Well that's alright then,'
everybody says, feeling awfully relieved.

31

The Mysterious Menagerie, Part Two

iv.

An African agitator,
sleeping now, snapping later –
living log with beady eyes,
a flash of jaws and something dies.

Antelope and sleek gazelle
know the dangers very well,
careful by the River Nile's
toothy and serrated smiles.

v.

Knitting hunter,
insect hater –
catch them now,
eat them later.

vi.

Orange as a sunset,
red as a pillar-box.
Entering the chicken-coop,
unwelcome as Goldilocks.

Don't Feed Your Teacher To A Dinosaur

Don't feed your teacher to a dinosaur.

They're tender you see, and easily upset.

And teachers are mostly made of gristle,
and when they're punctured they start to whistle,
and the noise is most upsetting
and it's very hard to get a vet in
to see a T. Rex with stomach upsets.

munch!

The End Of The Day

Staring into space
Just doing nothing much

I watch the clouds drift
Just doing nothing much

And I hear a sparrow sing
Just doing nothing much

And I hear a dropped pin
Just doing nothing much

And the clouds still float
Just doing nothing much

And the sky's still blue
Just doing nothing much

There is grass beneath my head
Just doing nothing much

And I should be in bed
Just doing nothing much

But it's an evening in the summer
Just doing nothing much

And it's warm and it's light
Just doing nothing much

And it's late but it's bright
Just doing nothing much

And I'm slipping into shade
Just doing nothing much

And it's the end of the day
Just doing nothing much

Nursery Rhyme Poem

I met a man upon the road
who looked a little like a toad
he had a broad-brimmed floppy hat
and in his arms he held a dog.

'A dog?' I said, 'That doesn't rhyme,
to carry that for all this time
is very weird – I'm all agog!
What you want, sir, is a cat.'

He looked me up and looked me down
and from the back and all around
and said, 'Sir, life is not a poem,
no, not at all and now I'm going.'

Summertime
(And I'm Glad I'm Not A Penguin)

If I was a penguin
I wouldn't like the summer.

There'd be no snow to slide in,
there'd be no ice to ride on,

and as it's getting hotter
there's not a lot a penguin like me can do

but fret,
and maybe also sweat.

Boy, it's hot!

A Lullaby For Oscar
October 2007

No one puts babies in trees these days,
  no one hoists cradles aloft,
the sway of a branch in the wind is unknown,
  insurers have warned us all off.

A mockingbird isn't a suitable pet
  to place in a cradle or cot,
they've claws and a beak and on top of which
  all the bird does is mock.

If your balance is poor don't sit on a wall,
  don't go to Gloucester if raining,
if you march up a hill for the old Duke of York,
  you'll only end up complaining.

We've learnt all these things the easiest way,
  from poem and story and song,
but one thing you'll find in the world outside
  is there's plenty left still to go wrong.

It's a dangerous place and it's falling apart,
  it's dark and it's cold and it's damp,
the climate is changing (that's partly your fault:
  you left on your nightlight lamp).

So, if you've got any sense, Oscar, me lad,
  you'll imitate old Sleeping Beauty,
ignore all the war and wrong turnings outside –
  and go to sleep now, it's your duty.

Midnight Feasting

I'm slipping on my slippers
and I'm slipping out of bed
and I creep into the kitchen
'cause I'm wanting to be fed

it's the middle of the night
and there's no one else around
so I can eat what I like
and I eat what I've found

there's half a pound of butter
and there's half a loaf of bread
and there're several dozen kiwi fruit –
I shove them in my head

through the hole in the front
that I like to call my mouth
and I swallow them directly
and they're all heading south

there're kippers in the fridge
and there's treacle on the side –
I dip the one into the other
and I send them for a ride

there's an aubergine I munch
and a tin of rice pudding
I open it and swallow it
and boy it is a good 'un

but now I'm getting thirsty
so I drink a pint of milk
mixed with mustard powder
and it slips down smooth as silk

and I follow it with cornflakes
and I follow those with mince
and I follow that with curry
and I give it all a rinse

with the cartons of juices
both the orange and the carrot
and in no time at all
I am squawking like a parrot

'cause I'm feeling very odd
and I'm feeling rather sick
and I creep back up the stairs
like an old man with a stick

and I climb into my bed
and I'm feeling rather fragile
like someone's been hitting
my stomach with a cudgel

I don't regret I did it though
I don't regret a thing
and while I'm turning greener
at least I get to sing

'I'm slipping on my slippers
and I'm slipping out of bed...'
and the rest of the song
is the poem you've just read.

The Visitation

I was trying to get to sleep
when I saw the flashing lights
and I heard that high-pitched humming
descending from the heights,

and the windows started to rattle
as the roar got ever louder
and then there came a crash
as dad's shed got turned to powder.

I tip-toed down the stairs
and peered out the cat-flap
at the interstellar transport
that had squashed the garden flat

and now a figure was emerging
from a bright white glowing hatch
and it had two arms and had two legs
and had two heads to match

and it was wrapped up in a spacesuit
that shimmered with unearthly powers
and it made its way toward the house
through the wreckage of mum's flowers

42

and it pointed a finger at me,
it must have seen me all along,
'Are you Master Jargle Flackenfrex?'
'Not me,' I said, 'You've got it wrong.'

'Wrong?' he said, 'Oh, bother,
blast, I've done it once again.
I'm sorry to have troubled you.'
Then before I could explain

he climbed back in his spaceship
and left the garden with a roar,
and all I wanted to tell him was
that Mr Flackenfrex lives next-door.

43

Jim and The Lion
A Cautionary Tale

(obviously after both Marriott Edgar and Hilaire Belloc)

Boys who chose to visit zoos
should tie the laces of their shoes
or if one's handy find a grown-up
to ensure their shoes are neatly sewn up,

for flapping laces, it has been said,
can lead to children being dead.
Take for instance little Jim
it was loose laces that did for him.

In the zoo he yelled and ran around
excited by all the things he'd found:
wolves and bears and snakes and rats
and leopards, tigers and other cats

of a large and toothy look
that Jim had read about in his book.
He ran toward the lion's pen,
his shoelace flapped, he tripped and then

he flew face first towards the cage
with a shout (not calm and sage)
and with a pop his head slid through
the cage's bars and stuck like glue.

His parents tugged at Jimmy's feet
but each tug they tugged met with defeat.
His ears were blocking his retreat
and so it was Jim became meat.

The noise Jim made, all his crying,
had woken up the sleeping lion
who slowly walked up to the lad,
then looked up at Jim's mum and dad.

The lion saw how Jim was stuck
between the bars by rotten luck.
Those two big ears, they were the problem
and so the lion started gobbling.

But a lion's not a tidy eater,
as eaters go you're probably neater,
but a lion always eats the lot
and never leaves any of what he's got.

Jim's parents couldn't blame the lion
for eating Jim, they were always trying
to teach the boy in many places
not to run with undone laces.

A Slightly Complaining Poem

Ants at a picnic
walking on the food,
didn't ask first –
very, very rude.

Wolves in the wilderness
howling at the moon,
I'm trying to sleep –
it's a racket, not a tune.

Icy white snow
falling all night,
no school tomorrow –
well that's all right.

Parrots Are Not To Be Confused With Dogs

A few tips.

If you take a parrot for a walk there's one thing you'll need
and that's a very long lead
because a parrot tends to fly
higher in the sky
than dogs do.

And when you throw a stick
the parrot may well perch on it
and if you shout 'Fetch'
bear in mind that the parrot's the only pet
equipped to quip –
'Fetch it yourself, buster.'

Pirates

The vegetarian pirate
has a carrot instead of a parrot,
which doesn't make much sense
but is handy if he ever needs
a nutritious snack halfway through the day.

Yo Ho Ho!
And A Bottle Of
Diet Coke Please,
If You Don't Mind,
Thank You Ever So Much...

(a poem for polite pirates)

Fifteen men on a dead man's chest,
the dead man growing flatter.
You'd only fit seven on
if some of them were fatter.

Bath Poem

If there's a fire in the house
don't scream and run and shout.
Just sit tight in the bath
and splash it all about.

The Last Doughnut

Only one last doughnut left on the side
when it hears me coming it tries to hide
but I'm too fast for it and I open wide
and there's one more doughnut on my inside.

The Mouse's Mistake

On the day that the mouse ate the elephant
we were all somewhat surprised
in part 'cause we'd fed the mouse earlier
and in part for the difference in size.

When questioned the mouse simply explained
he'd been bet by a man that he knew
and a fiver's a fiver he carelessly shrugged
and an elephant makes a good stew.

But that elephant, I tried to explain to him,
was our friend and our pet and on loan
from the zoo in Bristol who'd kindly allowed
him a weekend away for a roam.

When the weekend was up and we had to return
the elephant back to the zoo
we tied the hoover hose onto his nose
and hoped that the mouse would do.

Factual Poem About Animals

They're big or they're small
or they're hardly there at all –
they're animals

Mammals and reptiles,
toes can be prehensile –
on animals

Fur or scales,
fish or whales –
they're still animals

Herbivores and carnivores
and some of them are omnivores –
they're animals

Camels and donkeys,
deer and gnu,
snakes and tortoises,
sheep and caribou,
giraffes and ants,
and lions and fish,
octopus and eels,
all go squish
if you tread on them
(hard enough)* –
because they're animals.

* Please don't tread on them. It's bad.

The Mysterious Menagerie, Part Three

vii.
As big as houses end to end,
glimpsed and then it's gone,
an island for the mariner
he won't step foot upon.

A water feature fountaining
between the foaming waves,
an oily mountain sinking fast –
takes plankton to their graves.

viii.
Purr-bearer,
fur-wearer,
tail-tosser,
mouse-bosser.

ix.
At first a dot,
then a hop.

Giraffes Sitting Down

Giraffes sit down when they want to play cards
but they don't do it often because sitting down is hard
when your legs are as long as the giraffe's are
and when they see that they've got hooves the game never
  gets far.

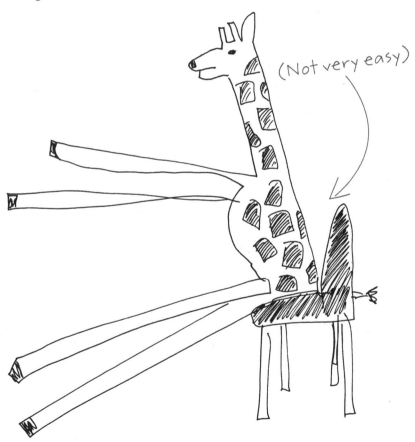

(Not very easy)

Polar Bears and Penguins

The polar bears over there
care for their hare
(a rabbit like thing they've adopted)
they feed it pear slices
and also fresh air
and the thing that's most nice is
they comb the hare's hair
and they pick it out outfits
the hare will then wear
to the parties it's chosen or opted
to go to.

The penguins are jealous because
they've never received the polar bears' love.
'But that's not surprising,' the polar bears say,
'Penguins are not often seen round our way.
If they were we'd be happy to welcome them in—
it takes a long time for our friendship to thin,
and there's always sardines when we open the tin.'

But the hare gets all uppish
and lowers his ears
which is how a hare displays his fears
when he hears
conversations like these,
since the hare's always near
to plunging despair
and is easy to scare
in the polar bears' lair
with the thought that their love
he might soon have to share,
and the bears might compare
his ears and his hair in a way most unfair
to the penguin's smart flair.
Oh it's all a nightmare.

Nonsense Poem

The world is full of nonsense
  it's just a crazy place
and it's not the owls and pussycats
  but the stupid human race.

A pea green boat makes perfect sense
  if you want to go to sea,
but to want to go to war is just
  a sheer stupidity –

but that doesn't stop the grown ups
  from inventing bigger bombs
and then from finding someone else
  to drop the damn things on,

just because they read a different book,
  or serve a different king,
or disagree minutely
  over some piffling little thing.

Give me a pig with a ring in its nose
  instead of a tank or a gun –
things that rhyme, I think you'll find,
  are warmer and more fun.

There are kids who live in poverty
  and there are kids who live on streets,
there are kids who're made to fight in wars
  in exchange for food to eat –

it happens and it's happening,
  and it breaks my heart to know
that here in the 21st century
  we've still a long way to go.

And the planet's overheating,
  the rhinos are nearly gone
and the cars are spouting poison...
  and I could go on and on.

So when they tell me I write nonsense,
  I laugh and say, 'That's fine,'
when I see what serious people do to the world
  if I make one person smile with a silly poem –
  is that really such a crime?

A Blessing on Sebastian
April 2006

This century's more yours than ours,
its darknesses, its lights,
the moment's peace between the wars,
its depths and maybe heights.

I see no easy way ahead,
we've failed to make it better,
you'll have to mend all our mistakes:
this war, the next, the weather.

The gift I bring, the gift I give,
is small, and cheap, and light:
it's made of easy-running words
to quiet you at night.

It's Hope, and Hope alone, I place
beside you in the crib,
there is a glimmer up ahead –
however darkly hid.

How To Avoid
Giants
Who Have Escaped
From Nearby Fairy Tales

It's no good looking out the window –
the foot of a giant
gives no warning from underneath.

It's no use putting up a sign –
unless it's a very high sign
that's big and easy to read.

It's no use trying to run –
a boot is as big
as a town to this thing.

It's no good trying to hide –
the boot comes squashing
not searching.

It's no good shouting a warning –
it's a long way up
and your voices are small.

It's no good worrying about all this –
there's nothing you can do
to alter the odds, no, nothing at all.

Poetry and The Dragon

If you open up my skull
  I don't have a brain in there,
underneath the skin and bone
  and reddish-brownish hair
is something rather different,
  something quite unique,
something I must feed with fancy
  several times a week.

There's a dragon in my brain-box,
  puffing fire in my head,
it's always hungry, always thirsty,
  always must be fed
on images imagined,
  on truthful things and lies –
this dragon needs some stoking
  to puff its fire in my eyes.

I feed it with the glitter
  of dew on a spider's web,
no sooner is it noticed
  than it's gulped into my head –
I see the leaves of autumn
  turn yellow and red and fall –
the dragon takes everything I see,
  the dragon eats it all.

He swallows the shouting of people,
  angry in the street,
the roar of a jet down the valley
  is gobbled up like meat.

The smell of new bread baking,
  the green of the meadow in spring,
the touch of a ghost at the back of your neck –
  the dragon eats everything.

He's kept alive by the world –
  by the sounds and the sights and the dreams,
he's got no ideas of his own, you see,
  but he's bulging at the seams –
he's fat with the pictures he's swallowed,
  huge on the noises he's heard –
from cheers in the playground football match
  to the squawk of grannie's bird –

that day when mum was sad with me,
  and the day that I fell in love,
and other days that passed so slow,
  the hurt of the bully's shove,
the dream that I set foot on Mars,
  the clatter of Beowulf's fight –
all roll around in the dragon's maw,
  sparking and letting out light,

and once in a while he puffs up a flame,
  bursting with all he's eaten
and the images rush, they flutter and roar
  like runners who won't be beaten
in the race of memory, the race of words,
  of poetry flaming anew –
and I write it all down, one way or another,
  'cause that's what poets do.

William's Song

Everybody stares at William's wings
(those two glorious and upraised things).
They sprout from his shoulders into the air
and whichever way he turns they are always there
and they're colourful, yes, they're coloured like light
and when the sun catches them they're ever so bright.

He sits in the morning on his windowsill,
he stretches for a moment and then he is still.
The sun warms the blood that runs in his wings
(those two glorious and upraised things)
and when they're awake he'll fly into school
but he walks in the corridor 'cause that is the rule.

And William's a brave boy, never afraid
of lions or tigers from a circus parade
or an owl that might eat children up with a snap
'cause William has defences displayed on his back,
two giant eyes, one on each of his wings
(those two glorious and upraised things).

A Poem About Why Some Dogs
Don't Like Having Baths

The dog in the bathroom is starting to bark,
he spent the afternoon playing games in the park,
chasing every stick and every thrown ball
and rolling in the puddles, both the big and the small.

When it started raining and the mud splashed up
he started rolling round like an excitable pup
who'd never seen a muddy, mucky bit of ground before.
He got as dirty as a dog can get, and then he got more.

But now he's come home, we're indoors in the dry,
and up in the bathroom he begins to cry,
as mum gives him a bath to dislodge the caked mud
and the twigs and the grit and she goes scrub, scrub, scrub.

But he makes an awful fuss and he makes an awful row,
and it's woof, bark, bark, yelp, grrr, yelp, growl,
and it's bark, yelp, woof, grunt, growl, bark, howl,
'cause she's got soap in his eyes and he can't reach the towel

because he's a dog and his arms are not long
and with paws instead of hands he couldn't hold on
to the towel anyway, so he barks and he cries
as any dog would who got soap in their eyes.

But he'll get his own back on mum in a minute.
When it's time to dry him off, she tries to begin it
by rubbing him dry, but he makes a quick break
and runs into her bedroom for a good

old

shake.

I Want To Be A Wallaby (Or A Kangaroo)

(to be read as fast possible)

I wanna be a wallaby
I wanna be a wallaby
I wanna be a wallaby
or else a kangaroo.

I wanna be a wallaby
I wanna be a wallaby
I wanna be a wallaby
or else a kangaroo.

A kangaroo can do what a wallaby can
and a wallaby can do what a kangaroo does.
If the kangaroos do what the wallabies do
the wallabies don't worry 'cause they do it too.

And I...
  wanna be a wallaby
I wanna be a wallaby
I wanna be a wallaby
or else a kangaroo.

I wanna be a wallaby
I wanna be a wallaby
I wanna be a wallaby
or else a kangaroo.

I'd bounce, bounce, bounce, bounce, bounce, bounce,
  bounce,
bounce all around, then I'd bounce some more,
I'd bounce, bounce, bounce, bounce, bounce, bounce,
  bounce,
I'd bounce to the park and I'd bounce to the store,
I'd bounce, bounce, bounce, bounce, bounce, bounce,
  bounce,
bounce, bounce, bounce, bounce, bounce, bounce, bounce,
I'd bounce,   bounce,   bounce,   bounce
and then I'd have a sit down because I might feel tired.

But I...
  wanna be a wallaby
I wanna be a wallaby
I wanna be a wallaby
or else a kangaroo.

I wanna be a wallaby
I wanna be a wallaby
I wanna be a wallaby
or else a kangaroo.

and so on and on and on...

The Mysterious Menagerie, Solutions

i.   Hippopotamus
ii.   Bumblebee
iii.   Penguin
iv.   Crocodile
v.   Spider
vi.   Fox
vii.   Whale
viii. Cat
ix.   Frog